INTRODU

Fish are the main source of food for many thousands of species. Humans have hundreds of ways to catch them, even more to cook them. It's no wonder that fish have evolved with such a glum expression, and incredible they've retained any sense of humour at all!

C..kie

famous last words.....

"i'll pop up and ask him when the tide's coming in!"

Sea Cow

cookie

Barry Whitebait

Cookie

big game fish

Cookie

FISHY DATE FLICK

"c'mon, a bunch of sharks just invited us to their feeding frenzy!"
Cookie

DOUBLE BASS

SURVIVAL: the art of confusion.

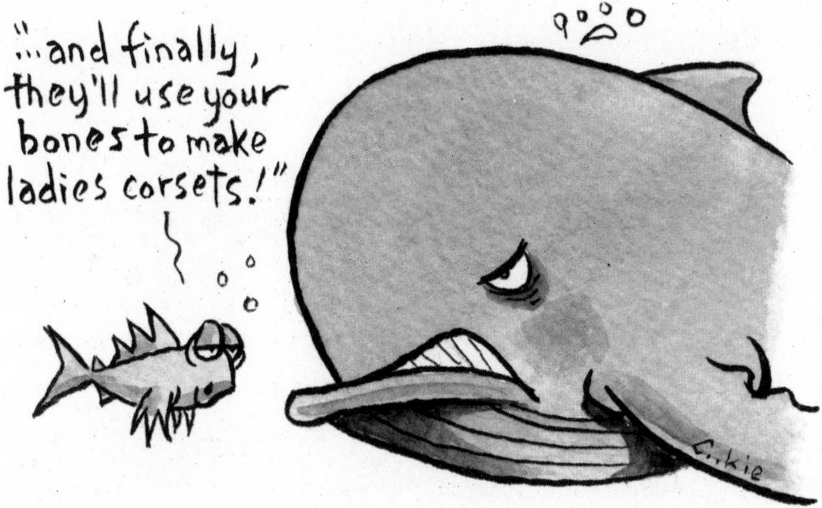
"...and finally, they'll use your bones to make ladies corsets!"

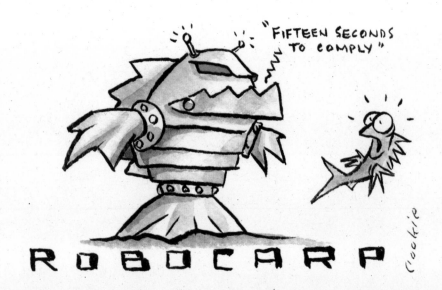

terrorpin!

Cookie

DRESSED CRAB

ALL PUFFED UP AND NOWHERE TO GO!

survival; the art of confusion.

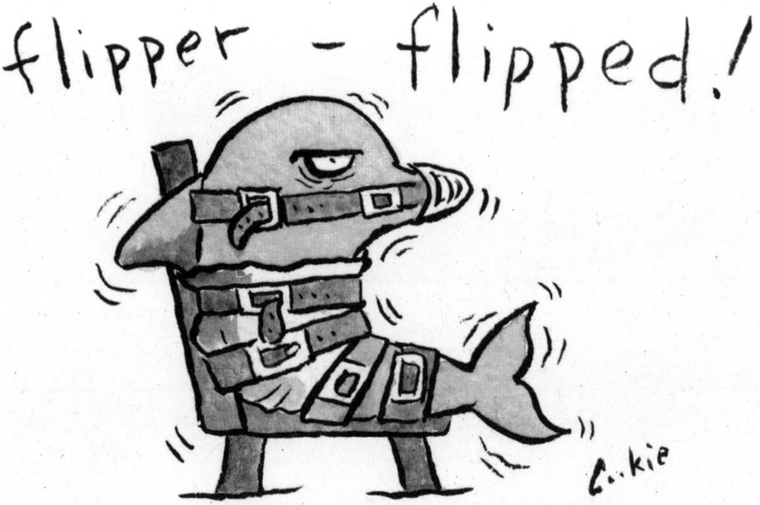
flipper - flipped!

cookie

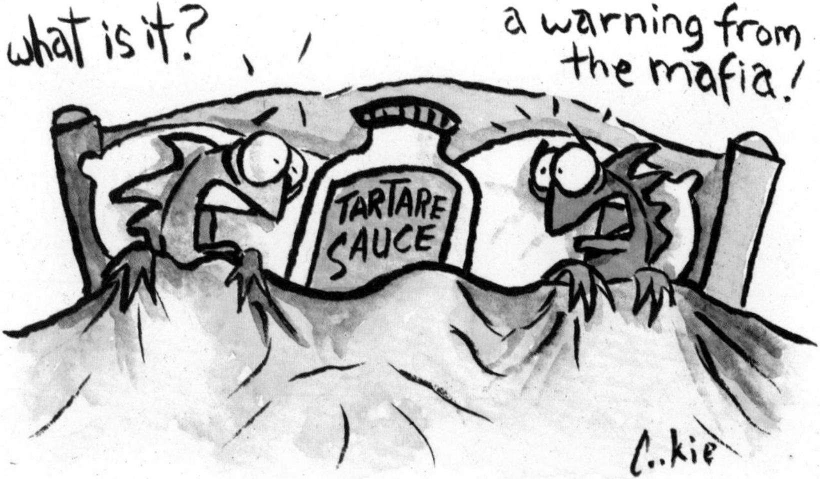
what is it?
a warning from the mafia!
TARTARE SAUCE

FUNERAL DIRECTOR

it was fathers last wishes that he'd be
pan-fried with lemon thyme and butter.

"your room looks like a bomb's hit it!"
"they're fishing with explosives mother"
Cookie

FISHY HORROR FLICK

"handball!" "it was a leg!"

more trouble flares in the octo-soccer league

Piano Tuna

THE INVISIBLE FISH

"ever since you've become invisible,
    you've been arrogant, cocky,
    ignorant and childish"

" you're talking
 to a table lamp!"

OLD AGED PENSIOMERS

on their zwimmer frames.

"i'll be back next week with a pod of leopard seals!"
THE ICE HOLE
NITE CLUB
ALE
HIC
PICKLED HERRING.
C.kie

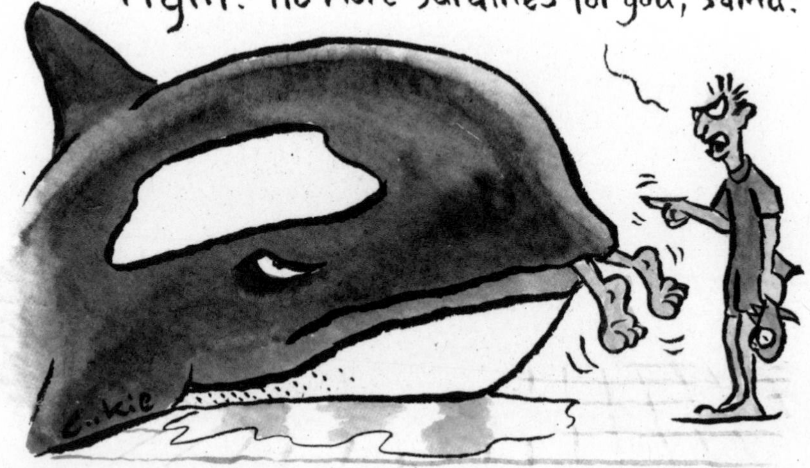

"right! no more sardines for you, samu!"

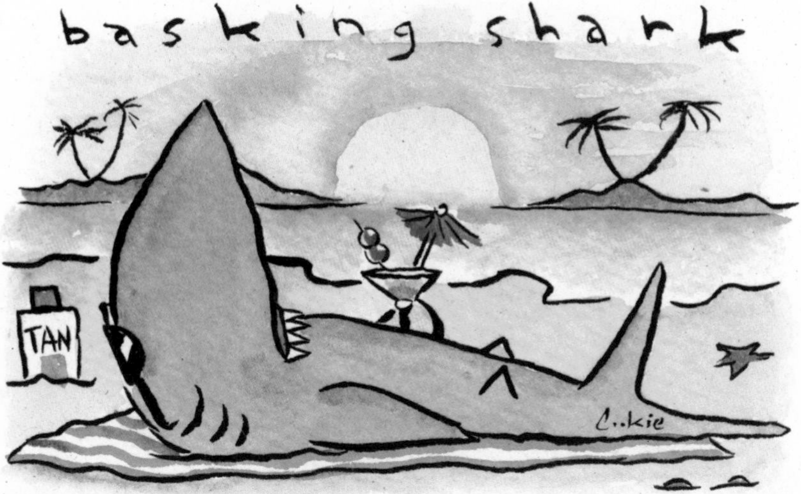
basking shark
TAN
C..kie

Rolling Stone - Crabs

i love the sea, father but i want to go on land as well!
see, he's talkin' like one of them amphibians again.

the problem with only one goldfish having
a **3** second memory span.

FISH PSYCHIATRIST

this 'swim with the dolphins' lark isn't all its cracked up to be!

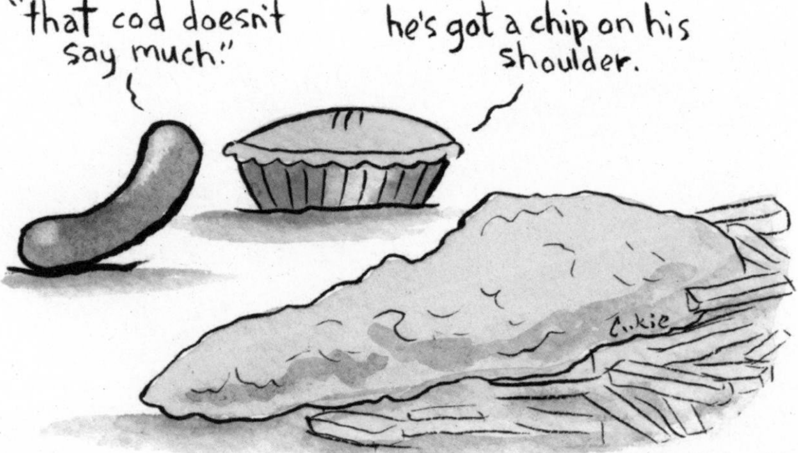
"that cod doesn't say much!"
he's got a chip on his shoulder.
C..kie

FISHY HAIR-DO'S . . .

demi-wave

permanent wave

PICKLED HERRING

"come on then, i'll take the lot of ya!"

"how long do we have to stay like this?"
"shsh, here comes a fisherman"
Polluted
Cookie

MEANWHILE... IN THE CRABSTICK FACTORY...
"hey, weren't you in a pop group?"
"yeah! we've been recently re-formed!"

tina   tuna